This Orchard
Baby and Toddler
Collection
belongs to

The Orchard Baby and Toddler Collection

The O
Baby and
Colle

chard

Toddler

ction

First published in 1997 by
ORCHARD BOOKS
96 Leonard Street, London EC2A 4XD
Orchard Books Australia
14 Mars Road, Lane Cove, NSW 2066
ISBN 1 84121 529 5

A CIP catalogue record for this book is available from the British Library
1 3 5 7 9 10 8 6 4 2
Printed in Italy

ACKNOWLEDGEMENTS

The editor and publishers would like to thank the following for the use of copyright material in this collection. All books cited are originally published by Orchard Books.

HUMPTY DUMPTY AND OTHER RHYMES from THE ORCHARD BOOK OF NURSERY RHYMES © illustrations Faith Jaques, 1986; MY CLOTHES from MY FIRST ENGLISH FRENCH WORD BOOK © text and illustrations Venice Shone, 1993; GETTING DRESSED from BABY DAYS © illustrations Carol Thompson, 1991; THIS LITTLE BABY'S POTTY from the book of the same name © text and illustrations Lynn Breeze, 1992; ONE HUNGRY BABY from the book of the same name © text Lucy Coats, 1992 © illustrations Susan Hellard, 1992; PINK SOCK, PURPLE SOCK from the book of the same name © text and illustrations Jonathan Allen, 1992; FIVE LITTLE DUCKS from the book of the same name © illustrations Ian Beck, 1992; THIS LITTLE BABY GOES SHOPPING from the book of the same name © text and illustrations Lynn Breeze, 1991; HEADS AND SHOULDERS from BABY DAYS © illustrations Carol Thompson, 1991; 123 HOW MANY ANIMALS CAN YOU SEE? from the book of the same name © text and illustrations Emilie Boon, 1987; HELPING from the book of the same name © text and illustrations Catherine Anholt, 1991; FOUR FIERCE KITTENS from the book of the same name © text Joyce Dunbar, 1991 © illustrations Jakki Wood, 1991; THE WEATHER AND ME BY FRED CAT from the book of the same name © text and illustrations Jonathan Allen, 1997; THE ORCHARD ABC from the book of the same name © text and illustrations Ian Beck, 1994; GOING TO PLAYGROUP from the book of the same name © text Laurence Anholt, 1991 © illustrations Catherine Anholt, 1991; BIG OWL, LITTLE TOWEL from the book of the same name © text and illustrations Jonathan Allen, 1992; MR BEAR'S PLANE from the book of the same name © text and illustrations Colin & Jacqui Hawkins, 1989; LITTLE PIGLET from the book of the same name © text and illustrations Nicola Smee, 1996; THE THREE LITTLE PIGS from THE ORCHARD BOOK OF NURSERY STORIES © text and illustrations Sophie Windham, 1991; WELLIE BEAR from TEDDY TALES © text Sally Grindley, 1993 © illustrations Peter Utton, 1993; BATHTIME from FIRST RHYMES © text Lucy Coats, 1994 © illustrations Selina Young, 1994; THE BIG SHIP SAILS illustration from FIRST RHYMES © illustration Selina Young, 1994; PLASTIC PENGUIN'S STORY from TOYBOX TALES © text Sally Grindley, 1996 © illustrations Andy Ellis, 1996; LITTLE CHICK from the book of the same name © text and illustrations Nicola Smee, 1986; THE CHRISTMAS STORY from the book of the same name © text and illustrations Nicola Smee, 1994. TWINKLE, TWINKLE, LITTLE STAR from FIRST RHYMES © illustrations Selina Young, 1994. Individual interior vignettes: page 1 (top) © Catherine Anholt, 1991, (bottom) © Selina Young, 1994; page 3 (top) Peter Utton, 1993, (bottom © Faith Jaques, 1986; page 4 (clockwise from top) © Penny Dann, 1992, © Selina Young, 1993, © Tim Warnes, 1996, © Debi Gliori, 1996, © Ian Beck, 1992; page 5 (clockwise from top) © Penny Dann, 1992, © Penny Dann, 1992, © Alan Snow, 1993, © Peter Utton, 1993; page 6 © Penny Dann, 1992; page 7 © Jane Ray, 1996; page 8 (top) © Alex Ayliffe, 1995, (bottom) © Ian Beck, 1992; page 9 (top) © Penny Dann, 1992, (bottom) © Sue Hellard, 1992; pages 16/17 © Selina Young, 1993; pages 18/19 (left to right) © Catherine Anholt, 1991, © Selina Young, 1993, © Sue Hellard, 1992, © Andy Ellis, 1996.

With special thanks to all the authors and illustrators who have contributed to the Orchard list.

All those who tend the Orchard know
Each tree must discover its own way to grow -
And on each branch the books ripen and glow.

Adrian Mitchell

"Within the covers of a loved book is an adventure of the spirit. . ."

Liz Waterland

What could be better than sitting with a baby or toddler on your lap enjoying the shared experience of reading a book? This is a cosy time alone together when the child will respond well to the undivided attention of the parent. And it is never too early to start!

The Orchard Baby and Toddler Collection was compiled with children of six months to three years in mind. It combines all the essential first learning and childhood experiences: first words, traditional rhymes, early learning concepts, counting and ABC, first experiences, and classic nursery and bedtime tales.

Babies love to point out shapes and objects and they delight in the physical pleasure of turning the pages to discover new surprises as they go through a book. In this way they very easily become familiar with the way books work. They respond quickly to the repeated naming of objects and to the catchy rhythms of traditional rhymes.

Toddlers will also enjoy simple stories and be stimulated by the bright lively illustrations, appealing characters and imaginative words. They love repetition which they can anticipate and join in with, so helping vocabulary building. And as they grow emotionally, they recognise feelings and situations familiar to them which will encourage them to talk about the stories.

A book can be shared at any time of the day but a warm and cosy story at bedtime is a wonderful way to introduce a young child to longer stories. And if you talk about the books you have both enjoyed, then reading should become a fun experience, a time together to look forward to.

Nurturing a love of books and reading from an early age will give your children a head start as they set out along the road of learning to read for themselves.

Happy reading!

Cont

ents

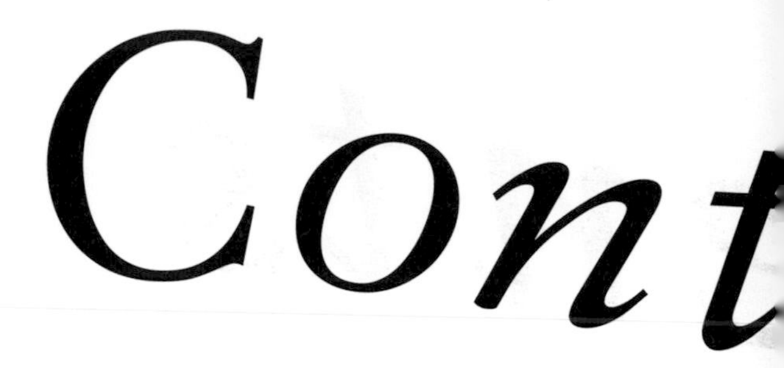
Cont

ents

✶

Ride a cock horse
To Banbury Cross,
To see a fine lady
Upon a white horse;
Rings on her fingers
And bells on her toes,
She shall have music
Wherever she goes.

*Bounce baby astride adult's knee,
hands firmly held.*

Games

Pat-a-cake, pat-a-cake,
Baker's man,
Bake me a cake
As fast as you can.
Pat it and prick it
And mark it with B,
And put it in the oven
For baby and me.

Say this rhyme while
patting baby's hands.

Going fishing in the deep blue sea,

Baby sits astride the adult's knee, hands firmly held.

Catching fishes for my tea;

Let baby down slowly between the knees.

Catch another for my sister,

Give a gentle pull upwards.

One! Two! Three!

Big pull upwards so that baby's held up high.

Row, row, row your boat,
Gently down the stream,
Merrily, merrily, merrily, merrily,
Life is but a dream.

Row, row, row your boat,
Gently down the stream,
If you see a crocodile,
Don't forget to scream!

Baby sits facing the adult on their lap, holding hands.
Gently rock backwards and forwards
in a rowing action.
Say the last line really loudly.

Two little eyes to look around,
Two little ears to hear each sound,
One little nose to smell what's sweet,
One little mouth that likes to eat.

Point to each feature in turn.

Round and round the garden,

Run index finger round baby's palm.

Like a teddy bear,
One step, two steps,

Walk fingers up the arm.

Tickle you under there!

Tickle under the arm.

Humpty Dumpty and Other Rhymes

from The Orchard Book of Nursery Rhymes

Faith Jaques

Humpty Dumpty sat on a wall,
Humpty Dumpty had a great fall.
All the King's horses and all the King's men
Couldn't put Humpty together again.

Ring-a-ring o' roses,
A pocket full of posies,
A-tishoo! A-tishoo!
We all fall down.

Hey! diddle, diddle,
The cat and the fiddle,
The cow jumped over the moon.
The little dog laughed to see such sport,
And the dish ran away with the spoon.

This little pig went to market,
This little pig stayed at home,
This little pig had roast beef,
This little pig had none,
And this little pig cried,
Wee-wee-wee-wee-wee!
I can't find my way home.

Baa, baa, black sheep,
Have you any wool?
Yes, sir, yes, sir,
Three bags full.
One for the master,
And one for the dame,
And one for the little boy
Who lives down the lane.

There was an old woman who lived in a shoe,
She had so many children she didn't know what to do,
She gave them some broth without any bread;
She whipped them all soundly and put them to bed.

MY CLOTHES

• Venice Shone •

• shirt •

• t-shirt •

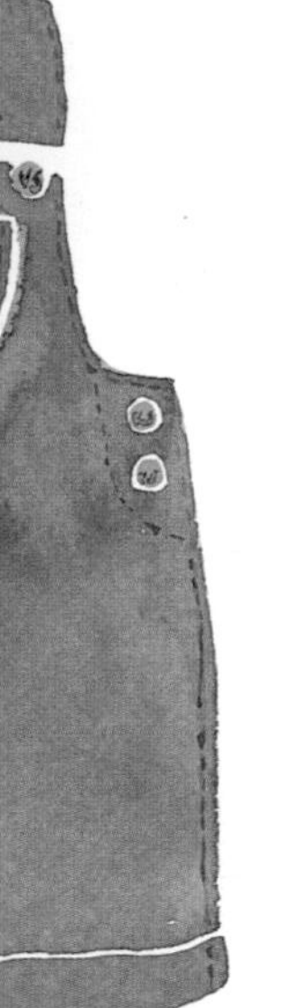

• hat •

• sandals •

• dungarees •

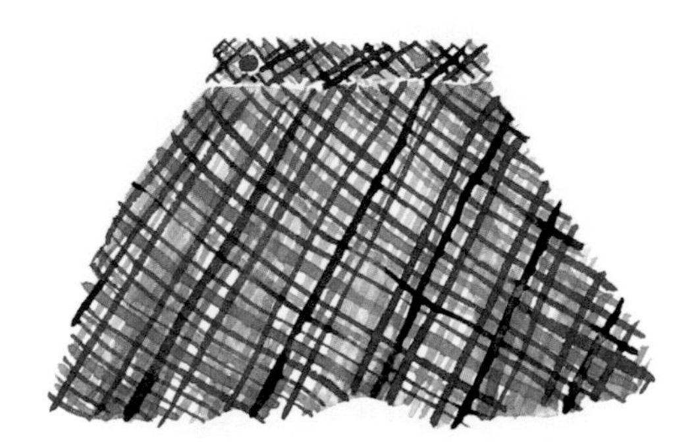

• socks •

• skirt •

pants
shorts
slippers
jacket
jumper
raincoat
boots
mittens

Getting Dressed

I can tie
my shoelaces

I can brush
my hair

I can wash my
hands and face

And dry myself
with care.

I can clean my
teeth, too

And fasten up
my frocks

I can dress all
by myself

And pull up both
my socks.

This Little Baby's

Potty

Lynn Breeze

This little baby's
getting dressed.

Mummy helps
with pants
and vest.

Running,
jumping, feeling
happy.

Nice and dry
without a
nappy!

Here's a boat
to sail the sea...

till this
little baby
wants a wee.

Run inside
as quick as
may be.

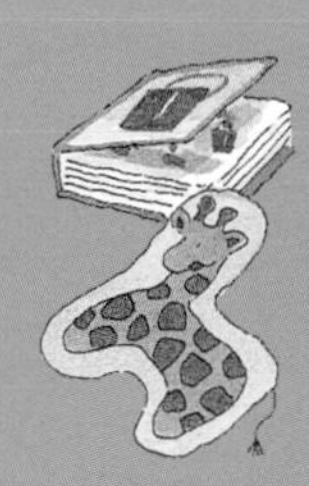

Use the potty,
clever baby!

One Hungry Baby

A Bedtime Counting Rhyme

Lucy Coats Sue Hellard

One
hungry
baby ...

Two front teeth.

Three dribbly chins
with bibs underneath.

Four bubbly bathtimes
To wash off the crumbs.

Five sploshy splashers
Five wet mums.

Six funny dads
Drying six button noses.

Seven big sisters
Counting tails and toeses.

Eight fat teddies
Ready for bed.

Nine soft pillows
Nine sleepy heads.

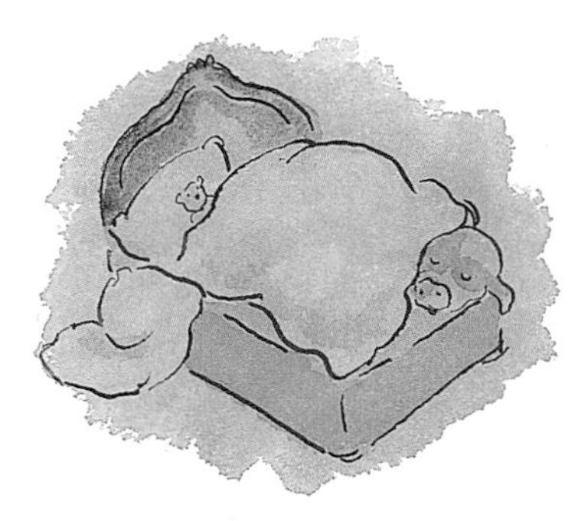

Ten good babies
Tucked up tight.

Twenty tired parents
Waving goodnight.

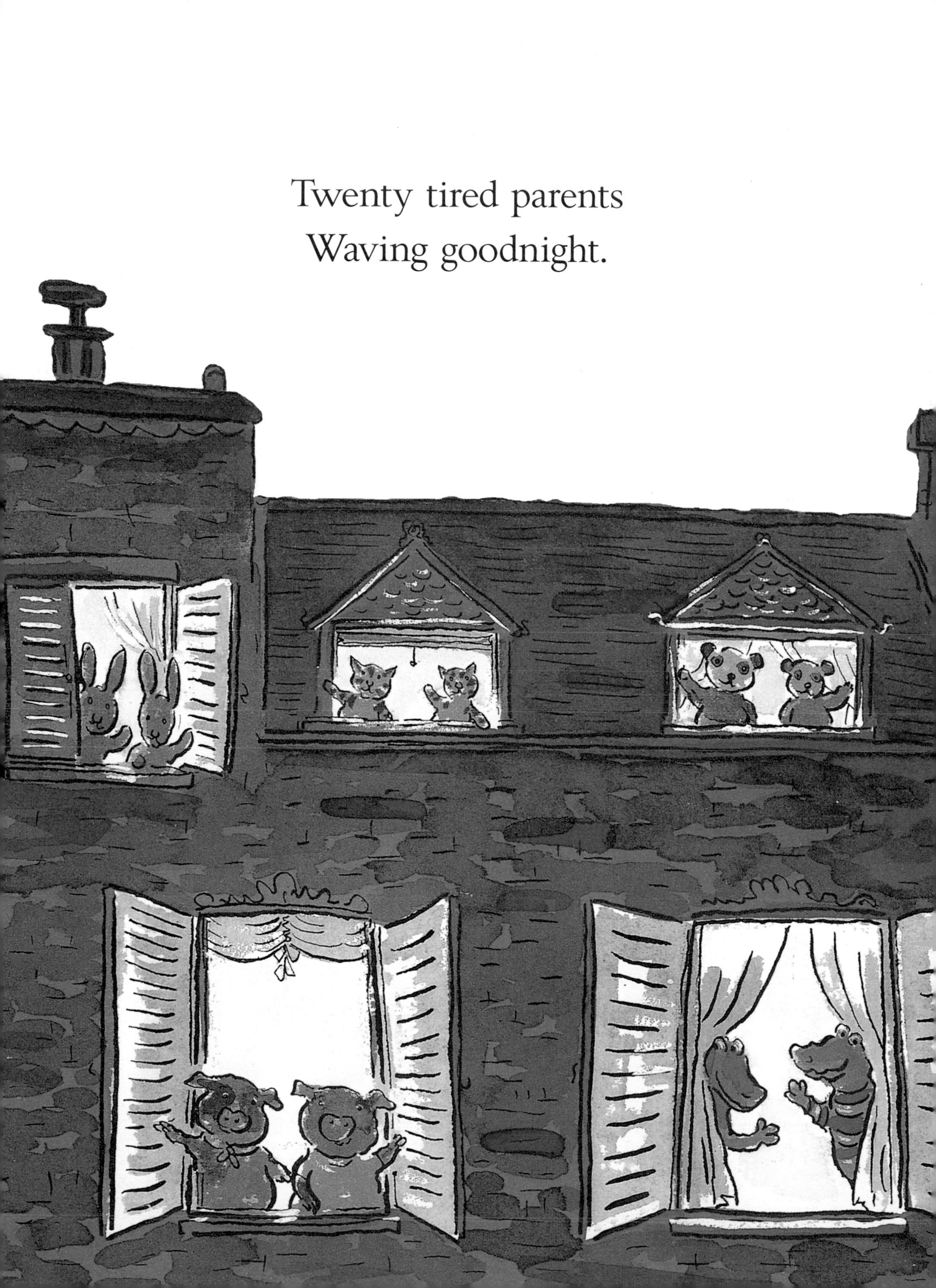

Purple Sock, Pink Sock

Colours

Jonathan Allen

Little Tabby's getting dressed. Pink sock...

Purple sock what comes next?

Big red trousers with red braces

New brown shoes with long brown laces

Favourite T-shirt
clean and white

Old blue jumper
much too tight

Yellow coat with
yellow buttons

Then a pair of bright
green mittens

Orange scarf and
a big black hat

What a
colourful
Tabby Cat!

Five Little DUCKS

Five little ducks went swimming one day,
Over the hills and far away.

Mother duck said, "Quack, quack, quack, quack."
But only four little ducks came back.

Four little ducks went swimming one day,
Over the hills and far away.

Mother duck said,
"Quack, quack,
quack, quack."
But only three little
ducks came back.

Three little ducks went swimming one day,
Over the hills and far away.

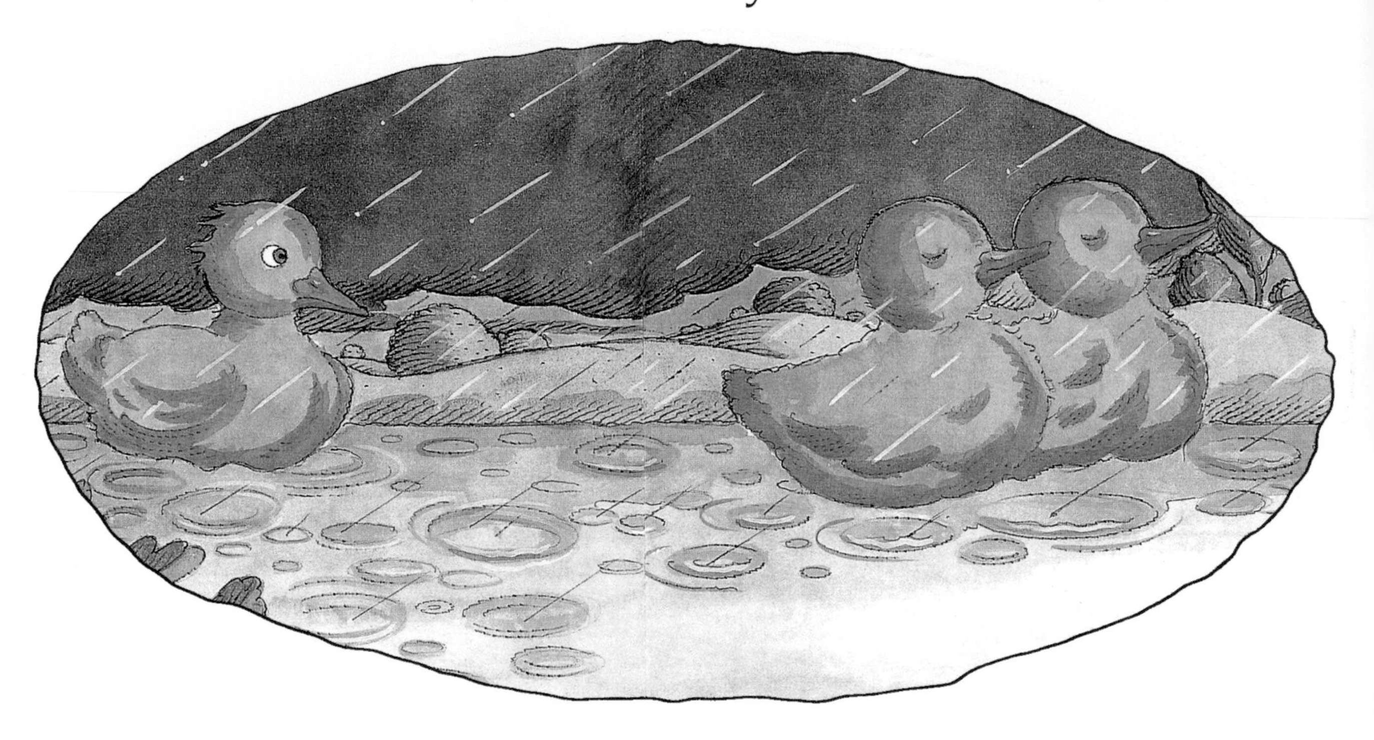

Mother duck said,
"Quack, quack,
quack, quack."
But only two little
ducks came back.

Two little ducks went swimming one day,
Over the hills and far away.

Mother duck said,
"Quack, quack,
quack, quack."
But only one little
duck came back.

One little duck went
swimming one day,

Over the hills

and far away.

Mother duck said, "Quack, quack, quack, quack."

And all her five
little ducks
came back.

This Little Baby

Goes Shopping

Lynn Breeze

This little baby
skips and hops

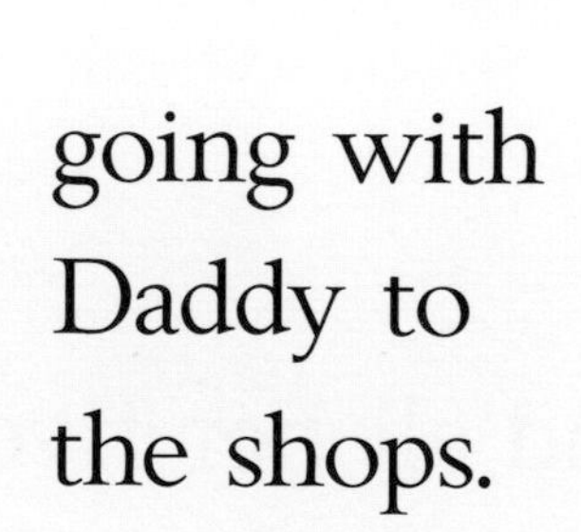

going with
Daddy to
the shops.

Here's a trolley
and the
shopping list;

apples, pears,
bananas: nothing
must be missed!

Big yellow cheeses
and biscuits
to crunch

honey for
breakfast and
beans for lunch.

Peep, peep,
goes the till.
Help to pack.

Carry the
shopping all
the way back.

Heads and Shoulders

Heads and shoulders
knees and toes.

And eyes and ears
and mouth and nose.

One · Two · Three How Many Animals Can You See?

Emilie Boon

One! Two! Three!
How many animals can you see?
Run, Rabbit, run!
That's just one!

Fox trots behind.
That makes two.

Duck paddles up.
That makes three.

Otter pops out.
That makes four.

Mouse joins in.
That makes five.

Owl flies above.
That makes six.

Hedgehog bobs along.
That makes seven.

Deer's waiting here.
That makes eight.

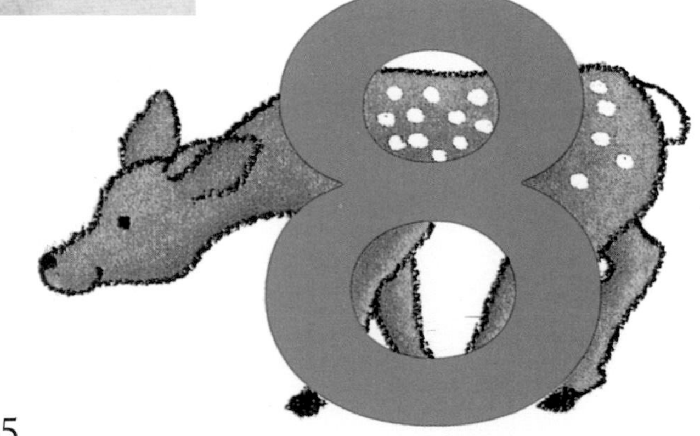

Squirrel scrambles on.
That makes nine.

One! Two! Three!
How many animals can you see?
Bear counts them all again.
Eight! Nine! Ten!

· Helping ·

• Catherine Anholt •

• tidying •

• sweeping •

• mixing •

• fetching •

• holding •

• cleaning •

• planting •

• choosing •

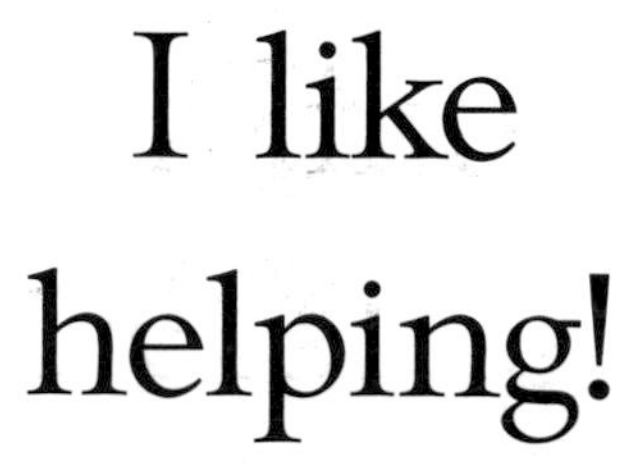

I like helping!

Four Fierce Kittens

Joyce Dunbar  Jakki Wood

Fat mother cat was asleep on her mat.
Said her four little kittens,
"There's no fun in that!"
And they went off round the farm to run wild.

Said the marmalade kitten,
spiking her claws,
"I am a terrible tiger!
I shall hunt hen out of her hutch."

And she tried to growl
(but she didn't know how)
She could only go...

miaow

miaow

And hen
went

CLUCK

CLUCK

CLUCK

Said the black little kitten,
with a glint in his eye,
"I am a panther on the prowl.
I shall frighten the pig out of his sty."

And he tried to howl
(But he didn't know how)
He could only go ...

miaow

miaow

And pig
went

OINK

OINK

OINK

Said the tortoiseshell kitten,
pricking her ears,
"I am a leaping leopard!
I shall chase duck into her pond."

And she tried to snarl
(But she didn't know how)
She could only go...

miaow

miaow

And duck
went

QUACK

QUACK

QUACK

Said the tabby little kitten, twitching her tail,
"I am a dangerous lion!
I shall make the sheep run down the lane."

And she tried to roar
(But she didn't know how)
She could only go...

miaow

miaow

And the
sheep went

BAA

BAA

BAA

Said the four little kittens, ever so fierce,
"We are tigers! Panthers! Leopards! Lions!
We shall scare that gaggle of geese!"

And they tried to roar,
To snarl, to growl
And they managed to go...

miaow

miaow

But the
geese went

HONK

HONK

HONK

Then a puppy came over to play.
Those four fierce kittens arched their backs.
Their fur stood on end. They hissed. They spat!
And that terrified puppy ran away ...

SCAT!

Said those
proud little
kittens,
"We didn't know
we could do
THAT!"

And they went back to their mother,
to sleep on the mat.

The Weather and Me

Jonathan Allen

by Fred Cat

FRED CAT'S
WEATHER

Here's me getting cold
Here's me keeping warm

Who's this in the mist?
Me of course!

THE
ORCHARD
ABC
IAN · BECK

A

B

A is for
alligator,
Aladdin,
acrobat,
apple,
anchor,
avocado
and ant

B is for bear,
Bo-peep,
basket, baby,
bird, balloon,
butterfly,
bricks, boat
and ball

C is for cat, clown, crabs, cake, candle, cliffs and clouds

D is for duck, drum and daisies

E is for elephant, envelope and eggshell

F is for fox, flute, fountain, fireworks, frog and fan

G is for gorilla, guitar, goose, grapes, glasses and grass

H is for Humpty-Dumpty, hippopotamus, house, hen and hyacinths

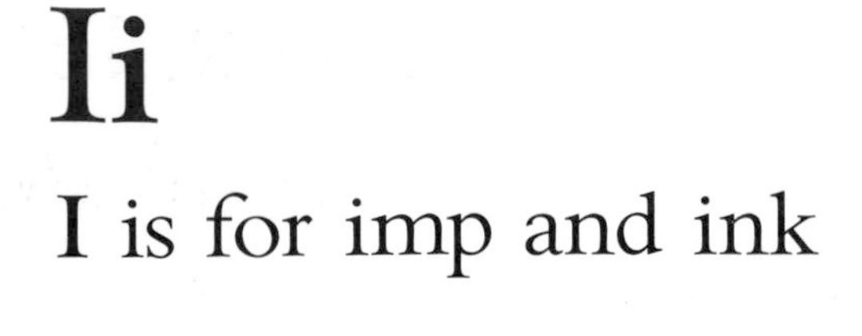

Ii

I is for imp and ink

Jj

J is for Jack and Jill, Jack and the Beanstalk and Jack-in-the-box

Kk

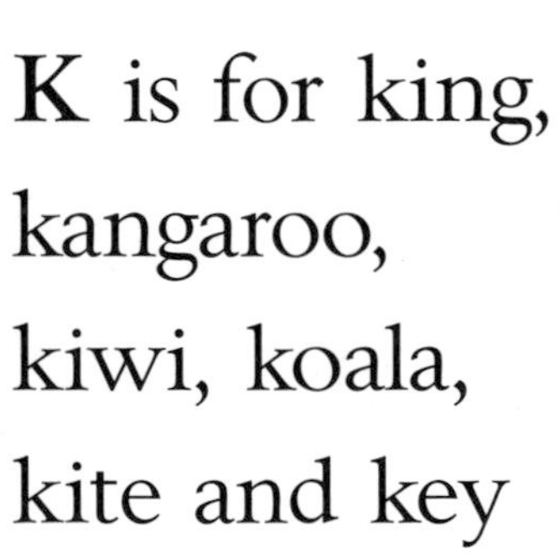

K is for king, kangaroo, kiwi, koala, kite and key

L is for lion, Little Red Riding Hood, lemons, lighthouse, ladder, leaves and ladybird

Mm

M is for monkey, mouse, mirror, mushrooms, moon, mask and magnet

N is for Noah's Ark

O is for Old King Cole,
ostrich, octopus, orange,
onion and owl

P is for Puss-in-Boots,
pig, pumpkin, parasol,
parrot, pears, pansies
and palace

Q is for queen,
quail, quill and
question mark

R is for robot, rocket,
rocking-horse, rainbow,
reins and rope

S is for sun, sea,
sand, starfish,
sandcastle, sailor,
spade and star

T is for toad, toucan,
teddy-bear, trumpet,
Tom Thumb, tree and
toothbrush

U is for unicorn,
umbrella and
Ugly Duckling

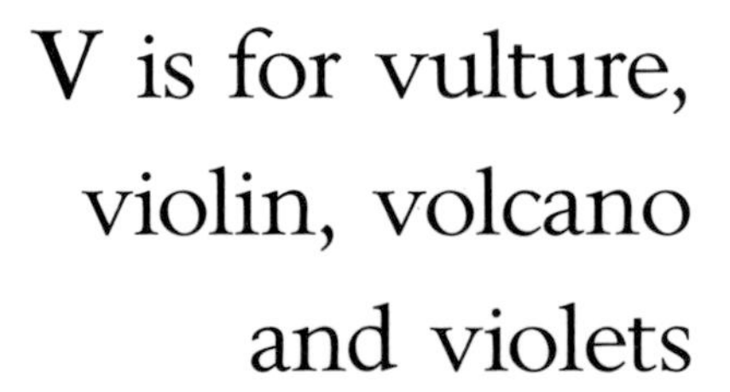

V is for vulture,
violin, volcano
and violets

W is for woodcutter,
woods, windmill,
witch and well

X is the ending for
fox and for box

Y is for yak, yawn,
yoghurt and yo-yo

Zz

Z is for zebras zzzz-ing

Going to Playgroup

Pictures by Catherine Anholt
Story by Laurence Anholt

Anna wasn't big enough to go to school. And she wasn't nearly big enough to go to work. But Mummy said she was getting too big to stay at home all day.

"It's time to make friends of your own," she said. "It's time to start at playgroup!"

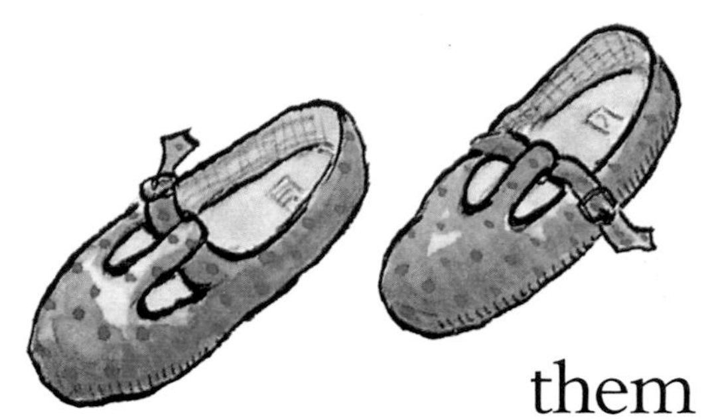

"You'll need new shoes for playgroup," said Mummy.

"Who will help me put them on?" said Anna.

"There will be a playleader, called Mrs Sams, and lots of other children," said Mummy.

"Supposing nobody likes me?" said Anna. She thought she'd take her sister with her. But babies don't go to playgroup.

"Perhaps I'll just stay at home," she said.

"Don't worry," said Mummy. "You'll love it when you get there."

"Hello," said Mrs Sams when they arrived. "What lovely shoes. Shall I help you put them on?

This is where we hang our coats and this is Tom. It's his first day too."

Mrs Sams took Anna and Tom to meet the other children. Some were having a story, and some were...

sticking

cutting

drawing

building painting and rolling.

Everyone was busy.

"Will you make something nice for me?" Mummy asked Anna. Then she went out of the door!

"Look, these teddies keep crying," said Tom. "They're being very naughty."

"Perhaps they miss their mummies," said Anna. "Shall we take them for a walk?"

Anna and Tom took their teddies to see ...

the rabbits

the guinea pig

the sand box

the water

the bikes

the slide

the home corner

the bookshelf

the dressing-up clothes.

Then the teddies stopped crying.
Mrs Sams needed
two helpers. All the
children wanted to help.
But Mrs Sams
chose Anna
and Tom.
"You're both
very helpful,"
she said.

Then all the children queued
for the toilets... but some
people couldn't wait.
They all had to wash
their hands. Tom forgot
to pull up his sleeves.

"Now walk back quietly," said Mrs Sams. But some children ran.

"And try and sit still," said Mrs Sams. But everyone jumped about. Anna sat next to Tom.

The children sang some songs, and clapped their hands, and then they all ran outside to play until it was time to go home.

"Hello," said Mummy. "Did you make something nice?"

"Yes," said Anna. "I made a friend!"

"Will it be playgroup again tomorrow?"

Big Owl, Little Towel

Big cat, little hat

Little cat, big hat

Big bear, little chair

Big chair, little bear

Sizes by Jonathan Allen

Big owl, little towel

Big towel, little owl

Big mole, little hole

Big hole, little mole

Mr Bear's Plane

Colin & Jacqui Hawkins

Mr Bear pushed his red plane out of the garden shed.

It was brand new and he couldn't wait to try it.

"I think I might go for a flight," he said.

Mr Bear's friends arrived.

"Hello, again!"
"Is that a plane?"
"Gee whizz!"
"Yes, it is!"
"Doesn't it shine!"

"Yes," said Mr Bear, "and it's mine!"

"Why don't you get in? We can go for a spin!"

But his friends were all too busy.

"I'm fishing today. I really can't stay."

"It's time we went
to put up our tent."
"Let's get off quick!
Planes make me sick!"
"Up in the sky?
No! Pigs don't fly!"

"Bye, bye! I must
get my washing dry!"

So Mr Bear decided he would go on his own.

"Let's have a look.
It's all in this book.
One, two.
Here's what you do.
Three, four.
Engine's roar.
Five, six.
Pull on joystick.
Seven, eight.
I can hardly wait!
Nine, ten.
Let's go then!"

With a mighty roar the little red plane leapt into the air!

"Wey hey! Wey ho!
Off we go!"

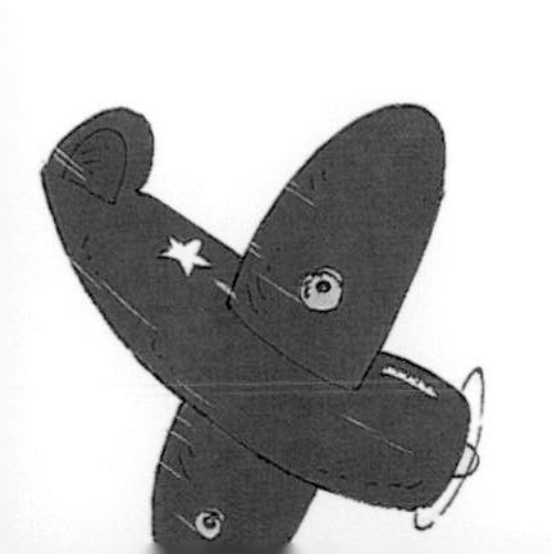

Round and round
the sky he flew
and then, far below,
he saw Croc, fishing.

"That's Croc
over there.
I'll give him
a scare!
Yoo, hoo!"

Mr Bear turned the plane towards Croc. It zoomed under the bridge and caught Croc's fishing line. Croc reeled himself aboard.

"Did you decide
to come for a ride?"
said Mr Bear.

"You gave me a fright!"
"You do look a sight!"
"Look, there's the rest of the bunch."
"Let's drop in for lunch!"

Rhino, Elly and Piggy were sitting by their tent. They looked up in horror as Mr Bear and Croc swooped down on them.

"Look out, Mr Bear!"

SCRUNCH! The tent was ripped from the ground.

"All aboard?" said Mr Bear.

"Silly old Bear! You gave us a scare!"
"Look at our tent!"
"The poles are bent!"

The little red plane went higher and higher ...

"OOOH! What a lovely view!" said Mr Bear.

Until ... PHUT!

The engine stopped!

"Hold tight!"
"Mummmmy!"
"My tummmmy!"
"Oh no! Down we go!"

At great speed the plane dived towards Hippo and her washing line.

"Watch how you go!"
"You'll hit Hippo!"
"Go over the top!"
"Oh, please! Can't
we stop!"
"LOOK OUT!"

Mr Bear's first flight ended up in a tree!
"Wasn't that fun?" said Mr Bear.
"NO!" shouted all his friends.
But they didn't really mean it!

Little Piglet

Nicola Smee

Little Piglet has just been born.
He has lots of brothers and sisters.

Little Piglet has a curly tail and floppy ears, and he likes to root around in the soil with his pink snout.

He rushes around and squeals loudly, but most of all Little Piglet likes his food!

When he's tired he flops down next to Mother Pig. "Grunt!" she says to her Little Piglet, "Grunt! Grunt!"

The Three Little Pigs

from The Orchard Book of Nursery Stories

Sophie Windham

Once upon a time there were three little pigs who went out into the world to seek their fortune.

The first little pig set off through the fields. He met a man carrying a bundle of straw.

"Please, man," said the little pig, "will you give me some straw so that I can build myself a house?"

"As much as you need, little pig," said he.

The man gave the straw to the little pig, and the little pig built himself a straw house.

In a little while a wolf came along and knocked on the door.

"Little pig, little pig," said the wolf, "let me come in."

"No, no, by the hair of my chinny, chin, chin, I will not let you in," said the little pig.

"Then I'll huff and I'll puff and I'll blow your house down," said the wolf.

And he huffed and he puffed and he blew the house down and ate up the little pig.

The second little pig went up the hill to the woods. There he met a man carrying a bundle of sticks.

"Please, man," said the little pig, "will you give me some sticks so that I can build myself a house?"

"As many as you need, little pig," said he.

The man gave some sticks to the little pig,

and the little pig built himself a wooden house.

In a little while the wolf came along and knocked on the door.

"Little pig, little pig," said the wolf, "let me come in."

"No, no, by the hair of my chinny, chin, chin, I will not let you in," said the little pig.

"Then I'll huff and I'll puff and I'll blow your house down," said the wolf.

And he huffed and he puffed and he blew the house down and ate up the second little pig.

The third little pig skipped down the lane towards the town. On the way he met a man carrying a load of bricks.

"Please, man," said the little pig, "will you give me some bricks so that I can build myself a house?"

"As many as you need, little pig," said he.

The man gave some bricks to the little pig, and the little pig built himself a brick house.

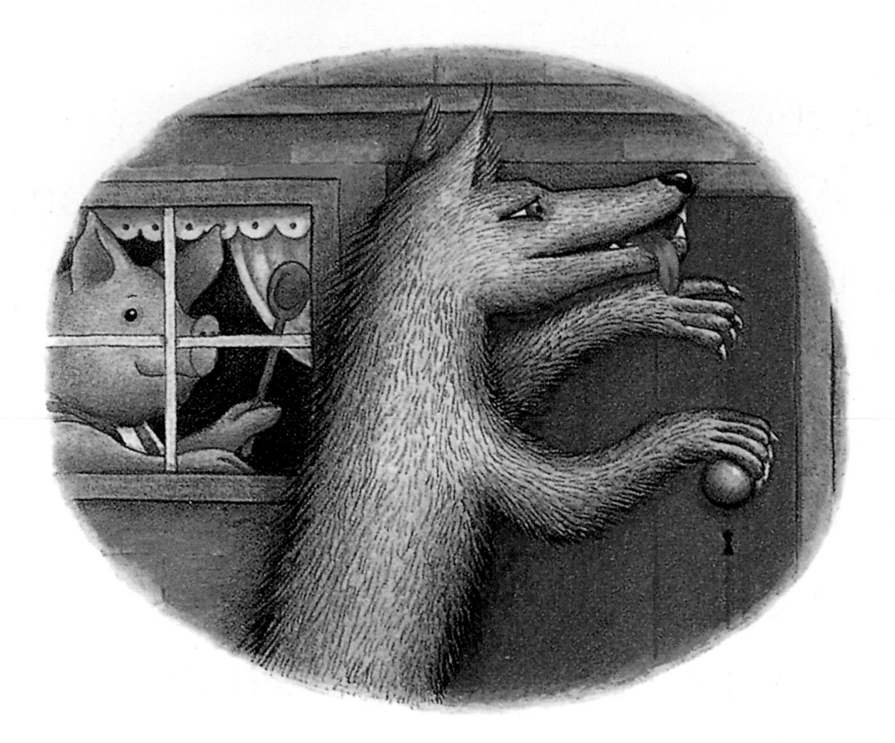

No sooner had the little pig settled into his new home than the wolf came along and knocked at the door.

"Little pig, little pig," said the wolf, "let me come in."

"No, no, by the hair of my chinny, chin, chin, I will not let you in," said the little pig.

"Then I'll huff and I'll puff and I'll blow your house down," said the wolf.

And he huffed and he puffed, and he puffed and he huffed, but he couldn't blow down the strong little brick house.

Then the wolf was angry. He sprang on to the roof and shouted, "Little pig, I'm coming down the chimney and I'm going to eat you up for my dinner!"

But the little pig was ready for the wolf. He had a big pot of water boiling on the fire, and he lifted the lid and the wolf fell right into the pot. Then the little pig slammed the lid on again, and that was the end of the wicked wolf.

And the little pig lived safe and snug in his little brick house for the rest of his life.

WELLIE BEAR

from Teddy Tales

Sally Grindley • Peter Utton

Wellie Bear wore smart red wellington boots and a bright blue plastic raincoat. But Wellie Bear wasn't a happy bear.

"Hrrmp! I'm fed up with being indoors," he moaned to himself. "I am a Wellie Bear.

I want to get wet. I want to jump in puddles. And I'm jolly well going to!"

The next day it began to pour with rain. When everyone had gone to bed and snores rumbled around the house, Wellie Bear tiptoed over to the window and climbed out on to the window ledge.

"It's raining, it's pouring,
They are all a'snoring,
And I'm going SPLASHING!"

With that, he slid down the drainpipe – WHEE! – and landed with a bump among the crocuses.

"I'm wet!" he shouted. "I've got a wet bottom and wet paws. Now for wet wellies!"

Wellie Bear stomped off down the path on a puddle hunt. The first puddle he came to was rather small, but that didn't matter to a bear who had never met a puddle before. He lifted one wellied foot up and – SPLASH! – down it came into the puddle. He lifted the other wellied foot and – SPLASH! – down that one came into the puddle too.

Left SPLASH! right SPLASH! left SPLASH! right SPLASH! left SPLASH! right SPLASH!

"My wellies are wet, my wellies are wet! That's what wellies are for!" yelled Wellie Bear, at the top of his voice. "Now for a bigger puddle."

Ten steps further on was a puddle that made Wellie Bear's eyes water. He had never seen such a huge puddle.

"Wow!" he shouted. "Count to three and in I go. 1 – 2 – 3 – jump!"

And he leapt into the air and landed in the puddle with a SPLASH! that soaked him to the fur, and filled his wellies with water. He got out of the puddle and jumped in again – SPLASH! – and again – SPLASH! A soggier bear you have never seen.

Wellie Bear was now very cold.
It was time to go home.
He squelched his way
back to the house.
But he couldn't
climb up the
drainpipe as easily
as he had slid down it.
It was far too slippery.

"What a silly bear
I am," he shivered,
"soaking wet,
freezing cold,
and stuck
out here."

He made his way round to the front of the house, crept under the doormat, and that's where he stayed until he was found the next morning.

"Perhaps I'll try the bath next time," thought Wellie Bear, as he hung out to dry on the clothes line, with his raincoat and wellies hanging alongside him.

Bathtime

Illustrated by Selina Young

Rub a dub dub,
Three babes in a tub
And who do you think got wet?
The daddy, the mummy,
The teddy bear's tummy,
So, hoppity, out you get!

Lucy Coats

The big ship sails on the alley alley oh,
The alley alley oh, the alley alley oh;
The big ship sails on the alley alley oh,
On the last day of September.

Plastic Penguin's Story

from Toybox Tales

Sally Grindley • Andy Ellis

Plastic Penguin was a bath toy. She used to stand on the edge of the bath waiting for Tom or Sarah to plunge her into the water. When they did she would whistle – PHHOOOO! – as the hot water flooded over her. It was always a shock, because penguins aren't used to hot water, even plastic penguins, but she loved being able to swim about.

When Tom and Sarah stopped playing with her, Plastic Penguin was put into the toybox. Sometimes they took her out just to look at her, but they never put her in the bath again and she really missed her swims.

One day Two Ton Ted shouted to all the toys, "It's snowing! Come and look, it's snowing!"

The toys clambered out of the toybox as quickly as they could and rushed to the window. They peered out and saw great white flakes floating past and falling slowly to the ground.

"PHOOOO!" whistled Plastic Penguin excitedly. She had never seen snow before, but she knew that snow was what real penguins liked more than anything else.

The other toys went back to the toybox and made themselves comfortable for the night. But Plastic Penguin watched and watched as the snow turned everything white. The garden didn't look like Tom and Sarah's garden any more. It looked like just the sort of place where even a plastic penguin would feel at home.

"Go and try it," said Two Ton Ted softly, "before it gets too dark. I'll watch out for you."

Plastic Penguin didn't need to be told twice. She waddled quietly out of the bedroom and down the stairs. She climbed through the cat flap, and there it was. Snow everywhere.

"PHHOOOO!" she whistled as she stepped into it and the snow covered her feet. "It's cold! But it's what penguins like best!"

She took a few more steps and nearly fell over. Her feet slipped and slid on the icy path – WHOOAAA!

Two Ton Ted chuckled from the bedroom window. "What's it like?" he called.

"It's cold and it's slippery and it's crunchy, and it's the most wonderful thing in the world!" shouted Plastic Penguin. "Come down!"

"No, thanks," said Two Ton Ted. "I like being in the warm."

"Watch this then," said Plastic Penguin. She took a few steps, then she dropped on to her tummy and tobogganed along the path – WHEEEEEEE! She stood up, turned round, and tobogganed back the other way – WHEEEEEEE! The third time, she went so fast that she couldn't stop.

"Look out!" yelled Two Ton Ted, but he was too late. Plastic Penguin whizzed off the garden path and straight into the pond – SPLASH! Then "PHHOOO!" she whistled, as the icy water flooded over her. It was a shock because plastic penguins aren't used to icy water.

"Are you all right?" called Two Ton Ted.

He needn't have worried. Plastic Penguin was swimming around and having the time of her life. Every now and again, she jumped out of the water and then plunged back in.

She swam on her front, she swam on her back, she twisted and turned and dived and leapt in the air – PHHOOOO! And then "PHOO!" she went, and "PH-", she was tired out. She dragged herself out of the pond and lay by the side, breathing heavily and shivering in the cold.

"What's the matter?" called Two Ton Ted.

Plastic Penguin didn't have enough strength to reply. Two Ton Ted rushed from the window, ran down the stairs, clambered through the downstairs window (he was too big to crawl through the cat flap) and began to make his way across the garden.

It wasn't easy. He slipped and slithered and fell head over heels. His paws grew heavier as the snow stuck to his fur. His whole body shook

with the cold. He tried tobogganing on his tummy like Plastic Penguin, but he just spun round in circles. So he crawled on his paws and knees, until at last he reached his toybox friend.

"Come on, Plastic Penguin," he said. "Let's get you back in the warm."

He took hold of her flipper and tried to pull her along, but he kept falling over. So he rolled her over on to her tummy, went back down on his paws and knees, and pushed her from behind.

When they reached the cat flap, Two Ton Ted lifted Plastic Penguin up and bundled her gently through the flap, then heaved himself in through the window.

By now, Two Ton Ted was tired out too. He knew he wouldn't be able to pull himself and Plastic Penguin back upstairs. So he carried her to the cat's basket, and that's where they spent the night.

Tom and Sarah never could understand how two of their toys came to be in the cat's basket. As for Plastic Penguin, she decided to wait for warmer weather before she went for another swim in the pond.

Little Chick

Nicola Smee

Little Chick has a strong little beak and is the first to break out of his egg.

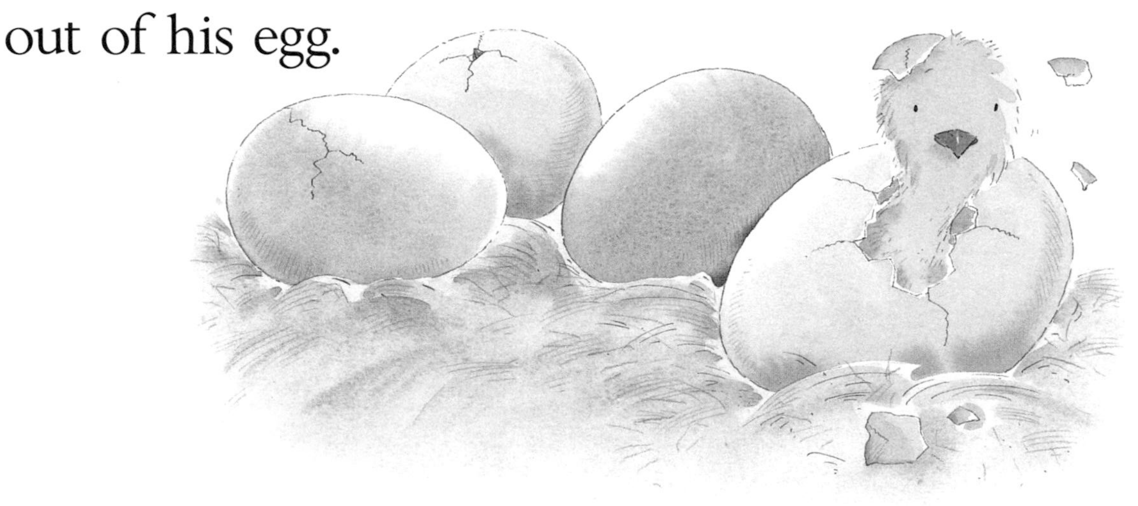

He is tiny and damp but can soon run around. And he does!

Little Chick drinks water and eats corn
and ruffles his fluffy yellow feathers.

At bedtime Little Chick snuggles up safe
and warm under his mother's wing.

The Christmas Story
Nicola Smee

Mary and a carpenter called Joseph lived in the town of Nazareth.

One day Mary was surprised by the Angel Gabriel. He told her that she was going to have a baby and that the child would be the Son of God.

Some time later, Mary and Joseph travelled to Bethlehem. All the inns were full, so they had to stay in a stable.

There, Mary gave birth to her son, Jesus. She wrapped Him up warmly and then laid Him in a manger.

An Angel appeared to some shepherds near by and told them the good news.

They went and found the baby Jesus and knelt before Him in wonder. The shepherds were so excited they told everyone that they saw, and they were filled with wonder too.

Meanwhile, three wise men from the East had seen a bright star and followed it all the way to Bethlehem.

They brought gifts for the baby
Jesus and knelt before Him
for they knew He was
the Son of God.

Twinkle Twinkle

Selina Young

★

Twinkle, twinkle, little star,
How I wonder what you are.
Up above the world so high,
Like a diamond in the sky.
Twinkle, twinkle, little star,
How I wonder what you are.

★